Guide to Affi
Astrophotography
Image Processing

2nd Edition

Dave Eagle
FRAS

Guide to Affinity Photo Astrophotography Image Processing - 2nd Edition by Dave Eagle.

Welcome to this second edition of my Affinity Photo astrophotography guide.

These guides developed from my extremely successful astronomy, astrophotography, image processing workshops, and 1-2-1 tuition, covering many techniques used to help the newcomer to become more proficient at using the software and achieving fantastic results.

There are so many ways of using image processing software and the methods shown within these pages is certainly not the only way to do things. Some people may have different approaches, but the workflows that follow within this guide are certainly the simplest way I have found to achieve fantastic results, processing my astronomy images using Affinity Photo (AP). I am constantly learning new ways of processing images, so this guide will be updated as new techniques are developed, or new tools added to AP. This guide is mainly written for the Windows version. Most of the techniques are the same in the Mac version, although some people have told me that some of the Plugins recommended cannot be used with it.

This second edition includes a few techniques I did not include in the first edition, as I was trying to keep the workflows as simple as possible. I have also included several new techniques I have picked after publishing the first edition.

Additionally, in February 2021, Serif released version 1.9.0.932 of Affinity Photo. This version included several new astrophotography tools, including stacking images (fits & raw files), background removal and image star alignment, which I have now included within this latest updated and expanded edition.

Dave Eagle FRAS. www.star-gazing.co.uk

Contents

Affinity Photo is a powerful and very cost-effective alternative to Photoshop. When running my astrophotography workshops, I was asked many times if Affinity Photo could be used to process astronomy images. Seeing how popular the software started to become with professional photographers, I decided to investigate its possibilities as an alternative to Photoshop. Most of the Photoshop workflows I used for my image processing were adapted to be used in a similar way using AP. This book is the result of those endeavours.

Affinity Photo is not totally dedicated astrophotography image processing software, like PixInsight, but it is extremely powerful software, especially with the latest astrophotography tools. Many Photoshop plugins can also be used that really can increase its effectiveness.

In this guide I will lead you through some of the image processing techniques I use within Affinity Photo so you can get great images from your images.

You may also have heard that you must use dark frames, flat fields, bias frames, and other such embellishments to produce great astronomy images. Indeed, the use of these techniques will certainly improve and enhance your images, especially for CMOS and CCD camera images. Many people are surprised to find that you do not have to use them to get a decent image. This is especially true when you are first starting out or use a DSLR. There really is no need to go to those lengths at that stage and make it more confusing than it needs to be.

My mantra is to use my image processing according to the **KISS** Method: **Keep It Simple Sunshine.**

In fact, virtually all the DSLR images I have taken over the year have not had these used calibration frames. I simply do not have time or the inclination to fuss about that much. In fact, when I have tried to apply them in the past with my DSLR images, they seemed to create more problems than they solved. However, I have found that at least flat frames are essential when stacking CMOS and CCD images.

What follows in this guide are Affinity Photo image processing workflows I use when processing my images. The techniques shown here are just as effective on DSLR, CCD and CMOS, monochrome, and colour images.

Affinity Photo.

Serif Affinity Photo was released in 2015, so is a recent introduction to the image processing software market. Like Photoshop, the functions buried within it are many and wonderful. In fact, many professional photographers are now beginning to realise that Affinity Photo is just as powerful as Photoshop.

This power is also its biggest downfall. Using the software and wandering amongst its many tools can be extremely bewildering and very intimidating, especially to the beginner.

Unlike Photoshop, which has an ongoing monthly subscription license model, Serif Affinity Photo is a single, and very affordable one-off cost of £48:99 (February 2020). Watch out though, as Serif frequently offer half price discounts and extended free trials.

There is a free 10-day trial available for you to test out the software and try it out to see if it will work for you. I did find that this was far too short a time to enable me to explore all its features fully.

Licensing and purchase details for Serif's Affinity Photo are here.
https://affinity.serif.com/en-gb/photo

When purchasing a license, you do have to specify if you want the Windows or Mac Version. The licenses are not interchangeable between the different operating systems, so a separate license is required for each.

There is also a cheaper iPad license version of the software available.

Once a license is purchased it enables the user to download and install a copy of Affinity Photo on as many PCs, Macs, or iPads as you like.

The software has a 14-day cooling-off period. If you do find the software lacking, you can get your money back if claimed within that time.

The license does not promise access to all future updates, but a lot of updates are free. This is especially useful if you also use it for everyday photography, as I do. It should therefore be able to handle RAW files from the latest cameras soon after the camera models are released. Major version updates may require additional payments going forward.

Like most software, it does come along with its own steep learning curve. When first introduced to some of these concepts it can very much feel like banging your head against a brick wall, not being able to quite get your head around what is happening. You just do not know how to tame the software properly to get just the results you want. No wonder astrophotography is seen as a dark art by those who have not been able to develop their image processing skills.

Having gone through this pain barrier with many different software packages many times, I know that light bulb moment, when something just "clicks" into the understanding, coming as a complete revelation.

Once that first peak has been surmounted, that feeling of progress then gives more confidence to start progressing further using more techniques. This guide leads you through the many workflows I use to help reveal the hidden detail in images using the tolls within AP. This will help get you over that pain threshold and well on your way to mastering the software and producing some fantastic astronomy images.

Affinity Photo has a couple of quirks you will need to be familiar with before starting out. There are several Personas which are used for different ways of working. Each Persona is selectable from the icons top left just below the main menu.

The main persona used for processing images is the first icon, The **Photo Persona** . The other Persona used when importing raw camera image files is the third icon, the **Develop Persona** . When opening raw images directly into Affinity Photo, the software automatically switches to the **Develop Persona**. Before the image can be edited, the **Develop** or **Cancel** button will need to be pressed to switch back into **Photo Persona**.

You can make different tools visible that you need regular access to visible from the main menu. **View > Studio >** Place a tick beside the tools you use regularly to make them visible.

Once visible, these tools can be dragged about to lock them into different parts of the Window. This makes them instantly available without having to click on a tab each time a tool needs to be used. You can see how I have set mine up in the image on page 20.

If you get in a mess with this, you can always reset the program to the default settings from the main menu:
View > Studio > Reset Studio.

Affinity Photo Shortcuts.
Although this guide is primarily written from the Windows version of the program, there is a list of both Windows and Mac shortcuts for AP here:
https://shortcuts.design/toolspage-affinityphoto.html

Actions, Plugins and Macros
There are quite a few Actions and Plugins available for Photoshop, these are not specifically written for use with Affinity Photo.

Actions.
Although many of the pre-bought Photoshop Plugins can be used in AP, you cannot create or use Photoshop Actions in Affinity Photo, so pre-bought Photoshop Actions cannot be used either. You can create your own macros within Affinity Photo which perform the same function as Actions.

Photoshop Plugins.
Plugins are not written to be used with Affinity Photo, but many Photoshop plugins can be used from within the software. Some plugins will install automatically into Affinity Photo if the installation is run after the installation of AP. Other plugins may need a little bit of gentle encouragement to become available as shown below.

When installed, Photoshop plugin s install themselves as 8BF files. To use plugins, the folder location of these 8BF files must be added to Affinity Photo. To do this, go to menu, **Edit > Preferences…**

In the new panel that opens, click **Photoshop Plugins.**

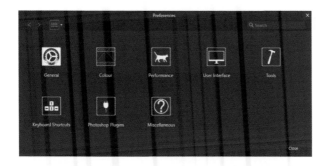

In the next panel, place a tick in the box **Allow "unknown" plugins to be used.**

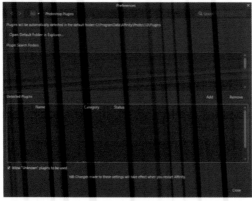

Click **Add.**

Browse your computer to where the **8BF files** for the Photoshop plugins reside. Serif do not recommend copying the files into the Affinity Photo Plugin folder.

Once browsed to the relevant folder, click **Select Folder.** If a suitable 8BF file is found within the folder, the plugin should now be visible in the lower part of the window.

Repeat for each location of your plugins. Some plugins may need more than one folder adding. The software will need to be closed and restarted to pick up the new plugins.

I would heartily recommend the following Plugins.
Affinity Photo does now include a Background Removal Tool in the latest editions. But these useful tools are still very useful for removing backgrounds and gradients.

AstroFlat Pro. Paid ($34:95 US). There is a 15-day trial available.
This plugin evens out the luminance levels in your astronomy images, while retaining all the detail. This is almost essential for processing images taken from my light polluted location.
http://www.prodigitalsoftware.com/AstroFlatPro1_News.html

I used to recommend **Gradient Xterminator** for Photoshop, but although it installed in Affinity Photo, I could not get it to work correctly without it keep asking for the license code each time it ran.
http://www.rc-astro.com/resources/GradientXTerminator

Other Plugins.
The **Topaz AI** Plugins are very nice, and work extremely well, but are not cheap. These include **Denoise AI** and **Sharpen AI**, ((£79:99) which both work extremely well with astrophotography images.
https://topazlabs.com/shop
After a while, they do start bothering you to pay for an upgrade.

Deep Sky Colours. Free (Donations Welcome).
Reduces the amount of green in a DSLR Image.
http://www.deepskycolors.com/archivo/2010/04/26/hasta-La-Vista-Green.html

DXO Nik Collection (£129). Expensive and not specifically designed for astronomical images, but the tools included, especially the HDR Tool can dramatically improve the appearance of many types of images.
https://nikcollection.dxo.com

Creating and Using Macros

If you are doing a technique often and apply it to lots of different images, it would be great to be able to set something up, so that a series of processing steps can be applied to an image from just a couple of clicks. When creating Macros, do not include any external plugins as part of the Macro as the macro will fail.

To set up a macro, open an image.

Recording a Macro.

To create a macro, you will need to make sure a couple of windows are visible. Go to the main menu **View > Studio** and check that **Library** and **Macro** are ticked.

If the tools appear floating above the image screen, they can be dragged into the area bottom-right of the window. Here they will show as tabs called Library and Rec (or Macro if selected).

To start recording a macro, click the **Rec** tab to make it active. The tab will now be called **Macro**.

Click the red dot to start recording. The Macro recorder is now recording everything that you do. Open the curves tool and apply a few curves to brighten the image. Remove the background. Then apply a Live Adjustment Layer to Sharpen the image, whatever! If you make a mistake, just go back a step. Although all your adjustments and keystrokes will be recorded, if you correct any mistakes as you go, these will not affect the result as you will have corrected these during the recording.

Once happy with the result, go back to the **Macro** Tool and click the white square to stop the recording. The recorded macro will now need to be saved.

At the top-right on the Macro Tool, click the **Add to Library** button.

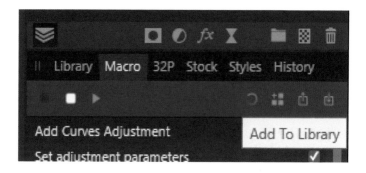

A box will pop up. Enter the name for the new Macro and press OK. It can be saved into a different **Category**, if required.

To find the newly created macro, click on the **Library** Tab.

Your Macro will be listed within the **Library**.

Applying a Macro to an image.
Open an image that needs the macro applied to it.

Scroll down the list of macros in the library to find the macro you want to apply to the image. Click the macro.
The macro will instantly be applied to the image.

This can save a lot of hard repetitive steps and make processing easier. The adjustments that need to be applied to one image to get the best out of it may not be appropriate to other image, so macros must always be used with great care. They are not always a one fit fix for all images.

Imaging Basics.

CCD's and CMOS chips are fantastic pieces of equipment. They enable you to take images under a wide variety of conditions.

It may come as a surprise to a lot of people that every single camera in production, even one-shot colour cameras, use a monochrome chip to record the image. This chip is composed of several light-sensitive pixels. The greater the number of pixels on the chip, the higher the resolution of the image.

1 megapixel = 1 million pixels.
12 megapixels = 12 million pixels.
24 megapixels = 24 million pixels.

The image produced by a 24-megapixel chip will create a much bigger file, taking up much more disk space than a 1-megapixel image.

While an exposure is being made, each pixel records photons that hit their surface and adds up these counts. The more photons that hit the pixel, the greater the value assigned to that pixel. A pixel that receives a small number of hits will record a much lower value.
At the end of the exposure, each pixel will have its own count. These values are read off the chip.

As the camera downloads the resulting image, a level of grey is assigned to each pixel. This can range from completely black, where no photons have been detected, to completely white, where a pixel has reached its maximum possible value. A completely white pixel has become saturated. On many Web sites, you may have seen a chart like this so that you can set your monitor to view images correctly. You should be able to see the difference between all levels of grey on your screen.

Complete black is on the left-hand side. This will be true for any pixel on the chip that has received no photons. On the right-hand side are pixels that have detected many photons and are saturated. There will be many pixels in between that have detected several photons somewhere between the black and white level, each at a different level of grey. The number of levels of grey shown between black and white in this example has only 14 steps.

Think of Pixels as Light Buckets

The term for a big telescope, such as a large reflector are affectionately known as a light bucket. The bigger the telescope, the more photons it collects.

I also like to think of pixels as light buckets. When an image is being taken, each pixel will collect photons and record the number of photons that hit it. A completely full bucket (pixel) is white. An empty bucket (pixel) is black. Every other pixel in-between will be a different level of grey, depending on the number of photons detected by each pixel (or how full, or not, that bucket (or pixel) is).

If we look at the histogram of an image it tells us a lot about the number of pixels at each level of grey.

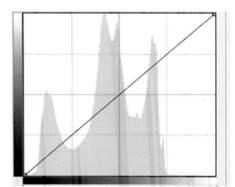

Along the lower axis, the black point is on the left-hand side. The white point over on the right, with varying levels of grey between each one.

The number of levels of grey that can be assigned to each pixel in the camera, will be determined by the bit depth of the imaging chip.

Different cameras will have different sensors installed, so the number of levels of grey produced in the resulting image is much more than the 14 shown above in the scale at the top of page 12.

Below are shown the depth of grey levels that can be assigned by different bit cameras:

12-bit image = 4,096 grey levels (2^{12}).
16-bit image = 65,536 grey levels (2^{16}).
24-bit image 16,777,216 grey levels (2^{24}).

As with the number of pixels, an image with a greater bit depth will produce a bigger file.

The peaks that can be seen in the histogram shows the number of pixels on the chip that are at a value of each level of grey. The more pixels with this value, the higher the peak appears.

When taking images, we want to avoid under-exposing (leaving lots of empty buckets – black) or saturating (over-exposing, filling lots of buckets – white), the pixels in our images.

Producing Colour images.

As previously mentioned, a camera chip will only produce a monochrome image composed of different levels of grey. For a one-shot camera to produce a colour image, the pixels need to be fed some colour information. This is achieved by placing a layer of coloured filters on top of the imaging chip.

This layer, called the Bayer Matrix, is designed so that a different coloured filter sits above each pixel on the chip. The Bayer Matrix has three different coloured filters; Red, Green and Blue. The camera knows which pixel is under which colour filter, so from that information produces a coloured image.

A different coloured filter lies above each pixel. A typical layout of a Bayer Matrix is shown below.

When the Bayer Matrix is in place, if a blue filter lies above a pixel, only light near the blue end of the spectrum will reach it. The same goes for pixels under the red and green filters.

This is where the inherent problems with one-shot colour cameras start to rear their ugly head.

This means that we are starting to stop quite a lot of light from reaching our imaging chip, as wavelengths away from the filters preferred wavelength never reach some pixels.

This will effectively make the image much dimmer, so a much longer exposure is required to get a reasonably bright image.

Most astrophotography (apart from the Moon, Sun, and bright planets) is performed using on very dim light sources, so the fact that a lot of light never reaches the chip already inhibits the cameras performance.

This is the reason a monochrome camera is much more sensitive than a one-shot colour camera.

One-Shot Colour Shift.

Added to this problem, the way the Bayer Matrix is set up also causes another issue. As you may be able to see from Bayer matrix, there are double the number of green-sensitive pixels than red or blue. This is because the human eye is more sensitive to the middle of the visible electromagnetic spectrum.

By allocating more pixels to be green sensitive, it gives a nice balanced colour in the resulting image, close to what we would see with our naked eye. As a result, images usually have a greener cast that they should have. In many images, this green colour shift may need to be removed in post-processing. More of which later.

Another loss of light at the red end of the spectrum is caused by yet another filter fitted above the imaging chip in a DSLR. This is the IR cut-off filter. Most imaging chips are very sensitive to red light. Images taken without the IR filter will have a strange red colour cast. The IR cut-off filter balances this colour, making the chip less sensitive at the red end of the spectrum, so again, the resulting image looks much more like how it would appear to the human eye.

Many astronomical objects, especially ionised Hydrogen Alpha (Ha) nebulae, emit light down that end of the spectrum, as this filter stops a lot of this light reaching the chip, an off-the-peg camera needs to make long exposures to record these. DSLR's can be modified (Modded), where the IR filter is removed, to make them more sensitive to this end of the spectrum. A modded camera will give a strange colour shift if the camera is also used for normal daytime photography.

All the images I have taken on my Web site and Flickr site have been taken using DSLR's without any modifications. As I use my cameras for all sorts of photography, I do not want to modify them. If I did this would severely restrict their use for normal photography. But this can be corrected later.

Taking and stacking images.

It is a fact of life, astrophotography, in most cases, is trying to record objects that are very faint. As well as the objects sending us only a small amount of light, the average one-shot colour camera as discussed above is further conspiring to restrict what we can record.

Thankfully, there are many techniques that we can use to enhance our images and reveal the true nature of the objects they can successfully manage.

Data is key.
The more data (light) you can collect, the better your image will be.

A good rule of thumb is to take as long an exposure as your tracking will allow.

Then take a lot of images to stack to contribute towards the result.

Unfortunately, it is a fact of life that most astronomical images will almost always be very under-exposed, even after doing all these steps as the objects we image are so faint, sending very little light our way. Light pollution does not help us either.

To get enough data for processing, we will need to do extremely long exposures, or stack many images to add data together.

My image processing workflow used to use Deep Sky Stacker, which is perfect for this purpose, plus it is free:
http://deepskystacker.free.fr/english/index.html

Affinity Photo now includes an Astrophotography Persona that can be used to stack astrophotography subs, including FITS images. In this guide I am showing how to do stacking with a mono image, but the technique is just the same using images from a one-shot camera.

Stacking Astrophotography Images.

To stack images, from the Menu, go to:
File > New Astrophotography Stack...

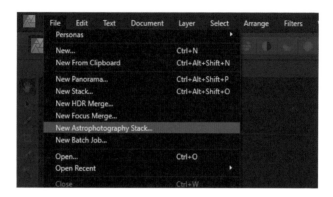

A blank window will open.

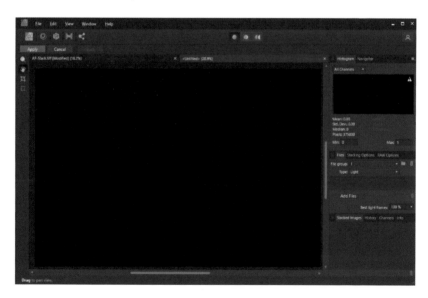

On the right-hand side of the window under the Files Tab, click the button
Add Files.

Browse to the folder where the captured subs for your image are stored. Select the light images to be included within the stacked image.
These can be raw DSLR images or FITS images taken by a dedicated astronomy camera.

If the subs taken for one image are located within a single discrete folder, you can select the folder itself. If you need to select only a few images from within the folder, you will need to select these individually.

Once the files are selected, one of the light images added will now be visible in the main window. The full list of files will be listed under the files tab on the right-hand side as seen in the figure on page 18. Clicking on each image, will give a preview of that image. If needed, inspect each image to see if the quality is good enough to include in the stack.
An image can be removed from the stack by clicking the eye off at the right of the image name. Alternatively, it can be highlighted and the dustbin underneath it clicked to remove the image.

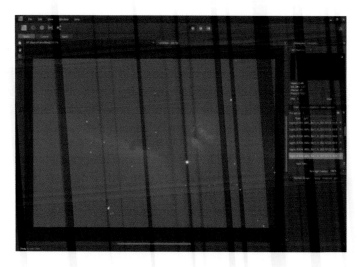

Images do not have to be the same way round. I have tested this on a set of images where part way through, there was a meridian flip.
Affinity Photo stacked all the images successfully.

All the light images are by default put in as members of **File Group 1**. Leave this on **File Group 1** as you progress. I have not yet investigated what adding other groups does or how these groups are used.

If the images are one-shot colour, under the **Raw Options** Tab, select the drop-down menu **FITS Bayer pattern:**

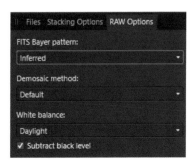

The default setting is **Inferred.** This should, in most cases, do the job. If you do find that the stacked colours are not correct, from this drop-down menu, select the Bayer matrix pattern that gives the best colour for that image and re-stack the images. You may need to play around for the best settings for those images.

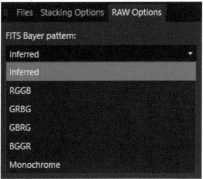

Once the light frames have been imported, if there are any calibration images that need to be included, click on **Type**, located just above the list of images. Select the type of calibration frames being added (**Bias, Dark, Dark Flat or Flat**) from the drop-down menu.

Click **Add Files** and go to the folder where these files are located to add them as before. Repeat this process to add each calibration frame set as required for your image.

Once all the Light frame Subs and calibration files have been added (if any), click the **Stack** Button at the top, just under the Persona menu.

The stacking process has started. A progress bar be visible.

When the stacking process is completed the stacked image will be shown in that same window.

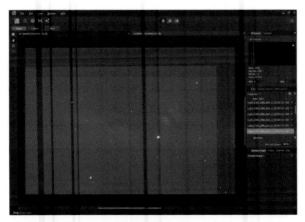

In this stack, the original captured subs were not quite aligned. This is visible as a darker band at the top and right of the stacked image. This will need to be cropped out later.

Click **Apply** top left of the window. The stacked image is exported to the Photo Persona, ready for post-processing.

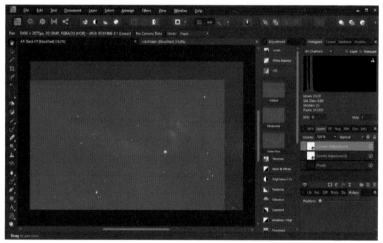

The stacked image automatically has a Curves and Levels adjustment layer associated with it, visible above the image in the Layers Window. These adjustment layers can be modified by double clicking on them to open them and any adjustments can be made directly on these. I prefer to start from scratch, so I delete these two adjustment levels before starting my post-processing. But you may want to use these as your starting point.

Working With Layers.

Layers is one of the concepts of image processing that takes a bit of getting used to. Many of the tools and techniques shown in this guide will produce layers. These will either be discrete images set in different layers, or adjustment layers. Adjustment layers need to be managed carefully, so that their effect is restricted to the image in a layer that they are affecting.

For example, if the curve tool is selected and used, once the tool is finished with, if the **Merge** button is not clicked to close the tool, the adjustment layer created by the curve tool will be left sitting above the layer that was selected when the curve tool was first opened, as seen in the image below.

Any changes subsequently made to that adjustment layer from the tool will affect the appearance of every single layer beneath it. As image processing progresses, you may find that lots of adjustment layers will build up, each one influencing the image to produce the overall result.

In many cases, you may need to only make an adjustment to a particular layer. Leaving the adjustment layer in that top position does not allow you to do this as it will affect all the layers beneath it as changes are made.

To force an adjustment layer to affect just a single layer, it can easily be moved, so that any adjustments only affect that single layer. This gives brilliant control and is a very powerful way of processing images.

To associate an adjustment layer to an image layer, grab the adjustment layer with the mouse and drag it onto the name of the layer that it needs to affect. A blue line will appear under the layer as it is placed in position as seen below.

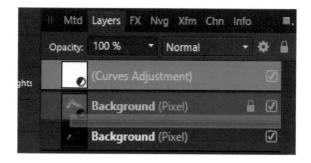

Once it is in the correct layer, release it and release it.
The adjustment layer will disappear. A triangle will appear beside the icon of the layer it is now associated with.

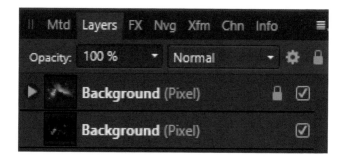

Clicking on the triangle will expand the layer so any adjustment layers associated with that image layer are visible, as seen in the image below.

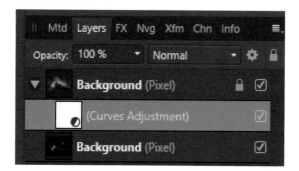

A double-click of the mouse on the adjustment layer will open it so further changes can be made. You can add as many adjustment layers to a single layer as you like, such as live adjustment layers etc. as discussed later.

Where's All That Data?

A typical stacked image will show an image like that shown below when opened in Affinity Photo. This is a one-shot colour image. If you would like to use this image and run through this work flow yourself, it is available for download from my Web page:
www.star-gazing.co.uk/AffinityPhotoDownloads

This image was stacked from 49x 1-minute subs and only really shows the stars around The Rosette Nebula. No trace of the nebula is visible. This can at first appear very disappointing after going through all that effort to capture that data.

So where is all that nebulosity? It is hidden in the image and will be revealed by careful post-processing of the image.

As we are in the Photo Persona, we can start processing the image further to get the data out and reveal the image hidden down towards the black end of the histogram.

Select **histogram** on the top right-hand side of the Window.

If it is not visible, from the Main menu, click:
View > Studio > Histogram and check the box.
The Histogram window should now be visible.

A monochrome image will show a single peak. A colour image show a Red, Blue and Green peak, lying close to one another.
The green peak is hidden in this histogram behind the other two peaks.
As most of our data is very faint, the peak in the histogram is way over towards the left-hand side, close to the black point. This makes it very difficult to see the faint nebulosity captured in the stacked image.
Most astrophotography images will have their peak over towards the left-hand side.
The nebulosity can be revealed several ways. Either get out and do even longer exposures and stack even more subs to add more data.
Unfortunately, we usually get limited time to take images, so if that is all you have got, the image can be carefully tweaked using AP tools to reveal the hidden data.

It is a relatively easy workflow to master but needs to be performed in as a series of orderly steps. Once you become familiar with this, it will enable you to become much more confident in trying out other tools and techniques and really develop (pun entirely intended) your image processing skills.

When taking images, never save or export files into JPG format. These files compress and will lose data. Export all images as TIF or PNG files.
As you go through the processing, I would recommend that you export your images as a different file name at each step if you want to save each step.

This will ensure that you never overwrite your original stacked file. If a different file is exported at each stage of the process, if something goes terribly wrong later, you can pick up the appropriate saved file and continue processing from that step in your processing.

There is a processing history saved in Affinity Photo can also get you out of a tight spot at times, but as these history steps are cleared each time you close the file, they will be lost if the file is closed.

Note: If you save a file with layers, be aware that the file size increases enormously with each layer added.

Let us get down to getting that nebulosity out of our image with some image processing with some careful adjustments with the Curves Tool.

The Curves Tool.

Open a previously stacked image into Affinity Photo, or use the downloaded Rosette image from my Web site:
www.star-gazing.co.uk/AffinityPhotoDownloads

The first step in my imaging workflow is to make a curves adjustment.
The Rosette Nebula image was taken with a Nikon D750 camera and is stacked from 49x 60-second subs through a 190mm Mak-Newt telescope.

Despite this being almost an hour's total integration time, only the stars of the cluster within and around the nebula can be seen, but no nebulosity. The image needs quite a lot of post processing to reveal the fainter nebula.

There will be some artefacts around the edge of the image from the stacking process. This is unavoidable. Press **C** to use the crop tool to remove the edges of the image so they do not affect the results later.
The amount you take off will depend on your camera and processing. Experience will help you to decide how much edge to remove. Double click on the image to complete the crop.

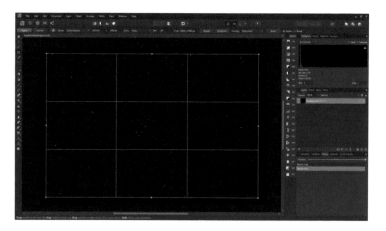

Once the image is cropped, press **Ctrl-M** to open the curves tool.

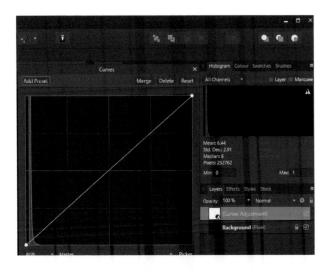

With the Curves Tool open, a bigger histogram will now be visible, where you will see the position of the peak. I have noticed that for some images, most annoyingly, the histogram peak position shown in the Curves Tool does not always match the other histogram window. It is sometimes shown either as an extremely small peak, or not at all.

If this is the case, you will have to use the other histogram window to judge the best adjustment of any tool while carrying out this step.

The white diagonal line running from bottom left (Black Point) to top right (White Point) on the histogram is the curve adjustment.

As it stands, it is unchanged, running from bottom-left to top-right.

We will use this line and move it around so we can stretch the image to brighten the hidden nebula to make it brighter in the image.

There are a couple of ways of using the Curves Adjustment Tool.

Click the **Picker** button.

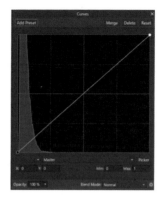

Clicking and holding the mouse button down on a part of the image will highlight part of the curve. This shows you the brightness of the pixels in that part of the image.

Keep the mouse button held down and move the mouse up and down. This will adjust the curve in the tool by following the changes made by moving that point on that part of the curve.

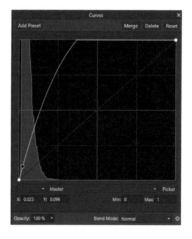

You can click on another part of the image that is a different brightness and do the same to adjust a different brightness part of the curve.

Alternatively, the curve can be adjusted by clicking on the curve within the curve tool itself and adjusting the curve shape directly from there. Adjust the curve, so that it looks something like the shape shown below.

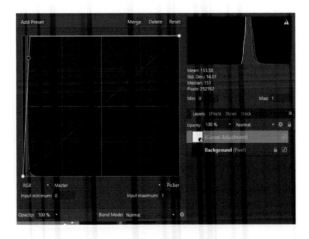

Do not click anything else yet. We have not finished adjusting the curve. Your image will have been over-stretched by doing this as you will be able to see in the image. In the histogram window, top-right, the peak has now moved well over half-way towards the right and has started to widen. Leave the curves tool open and look at the new adjustment curve that has been added. This is shown in white in the image above.

The right-hand side of that curve is now hitting the very top of the histogram window very early along the histogram. A curve adjustment like this must always be avoided. This new adjustment tells the software that everything to the right of that level of grey where it touches the top line will now be treated as white.

As a result of this, any data over to the right-hand side of that level of grey beyond that point will have been clipped up to white and will now be lost. It is always best that the extremes of white and black levels of any image are never clipped like this as this will lose data and a lot of balance will be lost from the image.

Even though there are no peaks visible over on the right-hand side of the histogram, there are some bright pixels there, such as brighter stars.

If OK is clicked now, this data will be lost for good and will never be able to be recovered. Another couple of adjustments need to be made to ensure we affect those brighter pixels as little as possible.

Click your mouse on the top of the curve to add a couple more points onto the line. Adjust the position of these points so it has a similar shape to the curve shown below.

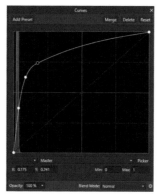

Now look at that new adjustment curve.

On the left-hand side where the curve is very steep, the value of those pixels at those darker levels of grey are being multiplied by a relatively large amount. What this means is that the faint pixels down towards the black end will increase in brightness. They will move towards the right-hand side of the histogram, effectively becoming brighter.

Over on the right-hand side in the brighter area, where the slope is shallower, we are hardly multiplying these pixels at all. The values of the pixels where we have stars and other bright objects have hardly been changed.

The image should now look something like this.

The colour and shape of the Rosette Nebula can now start to be revealed in the image. If the image has been taken in light polluted skies, there will also be some brightness in the background and possibly a light gradient visible.

If you are processing a DSLR image, do not worry if some green colouration is seen. This is caused by the colour channels not being correctly registered as well as background light pollution. We will remove some of this in the next step.

If working on a colour image, the Curves Tool can be used to adjust a single colour, by selecting this from the dropdown menu within the tool.

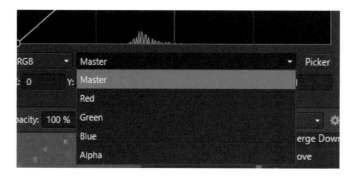

When happy with the curve shape and the effect it has on the image (**Do not be tempted to over-stretch or over-process it at this stage**), there are three things you can do to close the tool:

Clicking **Delete** removes the adjustment layer without applying the curve adjustment, so there is no change to the image.

Merge applies the adjustment and deletes the adjustment layer. When you feel more comfortable with managing the software, you may want to keep the adjustment layers intact instead of merging them. Doing so will enable you to go back and make more adjustments later in the process.

To keep the adjustment layer in place, close the tool by clicking the cross in the top-right of the tool. This closes the tool and applies the adjustment. But instead of becoming part of the image, the adjustment layer becomes a new layer, sitting above the image layer. Any adjustments made to this adjustment layer will be applied to all the image layers beneath it unless it has been associated with a particular layer.

If an adjustment layer has been associated with an image layer, it cannot be merged.

All the adjustment tools and adjustment layers in Affinity Photo work in a very similar way. If these adjustment layers are left in-situ, they can build up above the images as new tools and adjustments layers are created.

Each adjustment layer will have its own effect on the result of the image.

These can be left in place so that changes can be made later. Alternatively, they can be merged down, or the layers associated with them can be merged. The choice is entirely yours going forward with your processing.

The Levels Tool

Levels Tools adjustments are used in a similar way to the Curves Tool. I have found that it can be a very blunt tool, unless you are using very small iterative adjustments to make the changes.

Press **Ctrl-L** to open the **Levels** Tool.

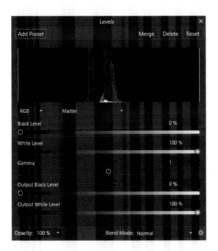

Looking at the histogram in the Levels Tool, in this one-shot colour image above, there is more than one peak is visible in the histogram. These three colour peaks should be aligned as a single peak. This means that one of the colour channels has lower values than the other two. This gives the colour shift that can be seen. In this case, it is the red channel, being closer to the left-hand side of the histogram than the blue and green peaks is darker.

Remember the IR-cut filter I mentioned earlier that cuts off the red end of the spectrum?

The peaks are also about midway across the histogram. This gives a bright background to the image. The aim is to get these colour levels adjusted so that these peaks are aligned properly, plus bring them a bit closer, but not too close to the left-hand side of the histogram.

There are three main controls within the Levels Tool.

Black Level – Adjusts the position of the black point along the histogram.
White Level – Adjusts the position of the white point along the histogram.
Gamma - Adjusts the position of the mid-grey point along the histogram.

Moving the Black Level to the right, clips data from the left-hand side of the histogram, darkening the image and background sky.
Do not move it too close to the start of any peaks visible in the histogram, or you will lose data.

Moving the White Level to the left, clips data from the right-hand side of the histogram, brightening the image. But I would advise in most cases, not to adjust this or you will lose a lot of your bright star data.

Moving the Gamma to the left, brightens the image. Moving it to the right, darkens the image. If you do use the Gamma adjustment to adjust the brightness of the image and draw your faint image data out, I suggest that very small iterative steps are used.

If working on a colour image, the Levels Tool can be used to adjust a single colour, if needed, by selecting this from the dropdown menu within the tool.

I never use the **Output Black Level** or **Output White Level** adjustments.

I usually use the levels tool to adjust images AFTER I have done most of my post-processing to do some final polishing to my images. Other people use the Gamma adjustment to draw out faint parts of the image, using very small iterative steps. When doing image processing, there are so many ways to achieve the same outcome.

The History Tool.

When processing your images, the steps you take will be recorded in the History Tool. This shows all the steps that have been taken when processing that image in that processing session. I access this bottom-right of the window.

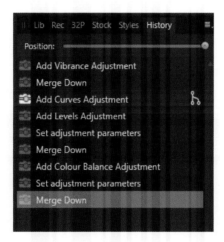

When a process is carried out, it will appear at the bottom of the History list. Clicking on any step above, goes back to when that step was done. If you do go back a step and then do a different process, any history beneath that step will disappear.

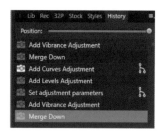

Remove Backgrounds & Gradients

This very handy tool, recently included with Affinity Photo, does allow you to remove the background or gradient from an image, without having to purchase a plugin like AstroFlats Pro.

In this instance I will be working on a DSLR image of the Andromeda Galaxy, taken through a small telescope in bright moonlight, which has a lot of background colour. This can be downloaded from my Web page:

www.star-gazing.co.uk/AffinityPhotoDownloads

Although this is demonstrated using a colour image, it can also be used on a monochrome image.

From the Main Menu, click **Filters > Astrophotography > Remove Background**.

A menu will pop up. A circle, which Serif call the Handle, will appear in the centre of the image. I am using the **M31-Background.tif** image for this.

At the top of the Remove Background Tool menu, tick the **Sample at handle position** box.

The image will now change as you adjust the Background Removal tool.

Grab hold of the handle on the image and move it into a part of the image that is part of the dark background sky.

On the top slider, labelled **Grey**, slide it towards the right. The further right this is dragged, the greater effect this has on the result.

Make sure that the circle is not located on top of a star, or part of a nebula or galaxy as this will darken the image too much. You may also find that the colour will change as the handle is moved around.

Keep moving the Handle about and adjusting the grey level within the tool until you get the best result.

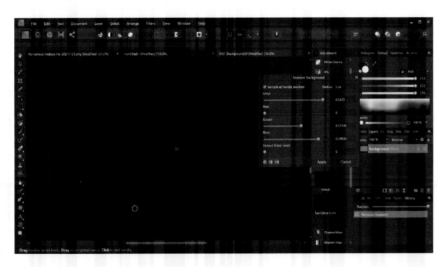

Make sure you choose a position where the colour looks about right. If the colour is slightly green this will be OK. This can be corrected later using the HLVG plugin.

In this image, a single handle is enough to remove the background, with the Grey level set about halfway towards the right. If the image being worked on has a gradient on it, extra Handles can be added by clicking on the image. As before, these can be moved about as required to achieve the best correction and remove the gradient. If a mistake is made and a handle added in the wrong place, it can be removed by clicking on it to select it and pressing **Del**.

It does not matter if the image is dark as this can be corrected using the Curves Tool shown previously.

Once happy with the result, click **Apply**.

The background or gradient should now be removed.
The image is now ready to be processed further.

Increasing Colour Saturation.

This helps bring out more colour in the images. This can be used on Deep Sky, Lunar, and planet images.

From the menu, go to **Layer > Duplicate.**

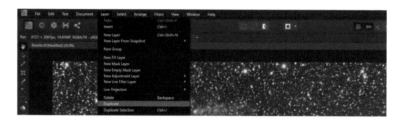

On the right-hand side of the Affinity Photo Window there will now be two image layers visible.

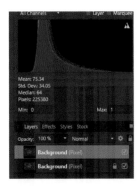

Click on the name of the new layer to rename this new layer to something suitable.

(I called mine **Luminosity Layer**, as this is what it will soon become).

Make sure that this new upper layer is selected by clicking on it.

At the top of the Layers window there is a drop-down menu which is set at the default of **Normal**.
From this drop-down menu, scroll down to select **Luminosity**.

This changes the upper layer into a luminosity layer.

Click on the lower layer to select it.

Click on the **Vibrance** Tool found within the **Adjustments** tab.

Move the Saturation adjustment to no more that about 20% – 30%.

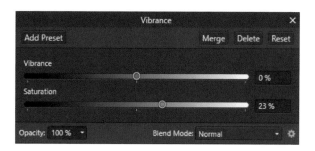

The colour of the nebulosity should now start to become more vivid.

Click **Merge.**

If you have enough data in your image, it may withstand a few more saturation increase steps. Watch the image as it is adjusted to make sure that the saturation does not become too garish.
You may notice that as the colour saturation is increased, the quality of the picture will degrade a small amount. The image will start to show a bit more colour noise and become a little bit grainier.

We rarely get something for nothing. Any adjustment made with the tools has potential to degrade the image as the data is stretched.

The image can cope with a bit of degradation so long as it is not stretched too far.

Even if we like the colour and have produced some colour noise, some of the original image quality can be restored. This is achieved by that upper luminosity layer, which helps us correct this.

Again, we are using the power of layers to get the best out of our image.

Click on the lower background image to select it.

From the menu select **Filters > Blur > Gaussian Blur...**

The more you move the Gaussian Blur slider towards the right-hand side, the fuzzier and blurrier the lower layer image becomes.

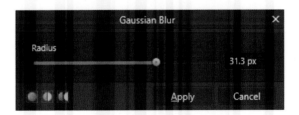

Click **Apply.**

In many cases this Gaussian Blur can improve the overall appearance of the image, removing some of the colour grain that was starting to show through into the image. You cannot see that the lower layer is blurred as it is only supplying colour information to the result.

The upper luminosity layer does not add any colour information to the appearance of our image, but it does dictate pixel brightness. Because the upper luminosity layer dictates the level of grey assigned to each pixel, despite the lower colour image being blurred, the detail contained in the upper luminosity layer is now dominating in the picture. The overall effect increases the colour but still retains all the detail.

To finish off we can apply a further curve adjustment.

Make sure that the upper Luminosity layer is selected by clicking on it. Press **Ctrl-M** to open the **Curves** Tool.

I normally put in a small amount of adjustment, bringing the darker end of the curve down a little and increasing the upper end of the peak a little, producing a shallow sigmoid curve.

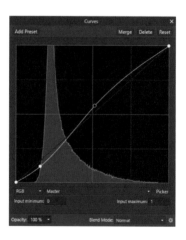

This adjustment is very subtle using this new sigmoid curve, but it does add quite a bit of punch to the image.

Depending on the quality of your image, you may want to make a few smaller saturation and curve adjustments to get the best out of your image.

Considering that the original stacked image looked like the image below, the transformation this software workflow has made is outstanding.

Converting Image Formats.

In some cases, you will need to convert files into different types.

You may need to use this to convert to different formats for some plugins to work. Some of them do not work on monochrome or 32bit images. If this is the case, the plugin will be greyed out and will not be available from the **Filters** menu, indicating that the image is not compatible with the plugin and the image will need converting.

To convert the image format (when required), from the main menu, click **Document, Convert Format / ICC Profile...**

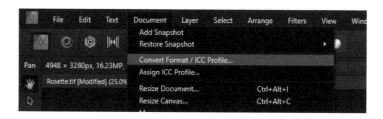

From the **Convert** menu that appears, select the appropriate image type required. In this case I am converting a 16bit Monochrome image so I can use colour data with it.

I am going to select the corresponding **RGB/16** format, then click **Convert**.

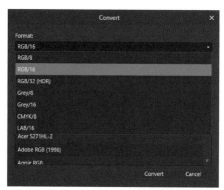

The image will now have been converted to 16-bit colour image format.

Removing Green Bias.

Remember the Bayer Matrix gave the DSLR image bias towards the Green part of the light spectrum? This is where the **Deep Sky Colours (HLVG)** plugin now comes in.

This image of the Rosette Nebula does not require much green removal, but many other astronomy images will.

If the plugin has been copied to the correct folder and activated, it is selectable from the menu.

Once the image has been processed click,
Filters > Plugins > DeepSkyColours > HLVG...

This opens the HLVG Plugin.

I normally use a Medium setting for my DSLR. Play around with the settings to find out what works best for your images. Click **OK**.

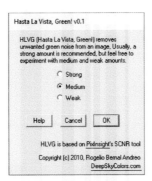

Any green bias in the image should have been removed.

If using a Luminosity layer above the colour image as shown above, this plugin will need to be applied to the lower colour image layer to work.

Layer Masking.

When many people start doing astrophotography, they always start with the brightest objects in the sky. M42, the Great Orion Nebula, or M31, the Andromeda Galaxy are fine examples. Many fine images can be seen online of people's first images of these objects. Unfortunately, these objects come with their own issues. Because parts of these objects are so bright, if we want to reveal some of the fainter features, the brighter parts become totally over-exposed and burnt out, so everything is white. Detail around the trapezium is totally lost.

The images below clearly show the problem.

M42 – Short exposure.   M42 – Long exposure.

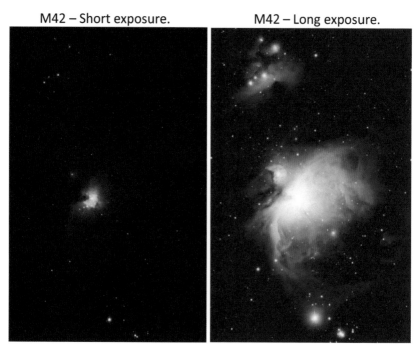

Layer masking is the way forward in combining multiple images that show both the faint extensions and still show detail in the brighter portions. Let us see how Layer Masking works.

Before we tackle something as complex as M42, we will start with an image of M13, the Great Hercules Globular Cluster.

If you want to process this same image, it can be downloaded from my Web page: **www.star-gazing.co.uk/AffinityPhotoDownloads**

Open the M13_Stack image in Affinity Photo.

At this stage, the stacked image looks quite dark.

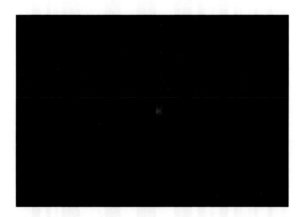

As in the Rosette image used previously, all the techniques above can be used to help bring out fainter stars. Do not over stretch the image so that the centre starts to over-saturate, and the central stars merge.

Use **HLVG** to get rid of any green hue, if required.

The resulting image should now appear something like the image below. The image is much brighter, with stars visible right into the core of the cluster.

This image looks a great deal better, but there is a lot more detail and many fainter stars around the edges of the globular cluster waiting to be revealed. If we were to do a repeat curve adjustment to reveal these stars, the stars in the bright centre of the globular cluster will start to burn out. That detail will be forever lost, creating a blank white centre to the cluster.

This can be avoided by using a technique called **Layer masking.**
This will enable us to hold back brighter parts of the image to keep stars visible in the centre.

Creating the Layer Mask.
With the M13 image still open in Affinity Photo, from the menu, click **Layer, Duplicate.**

A new image layer identical to the lower one will have been created.

Once the layer has been duplicated, click on the little box on right-hand side of the upper layer to hide it.

You will not notice any change in the look of the image at this stage.

Click on the lower layer to select it.

Press **Ctrl-M** as before to apply a curve adjustment on the lower layer. This time do not worry if the stars in the central core of the globular start to merge into one another and become over-exposed.

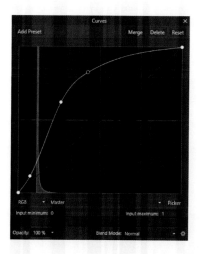

The image should now look something like the one below.

Many fainter stars around the outer edge of the cluster and other deep sky objects are nicely visible.

The centre of the cluster is now looking totally white and completely washed out. The central stars have merged, but that is OK. Click **Merge.**

It is now time to start taming the centre of the cluster to get the stars in the central core stars back into view. This is where the true power of layer masking really comes into its own.

Make sure that the lower layer with the burnt-out M13 core is still selected.

From the main menu, click **Layer > Duplicate.**

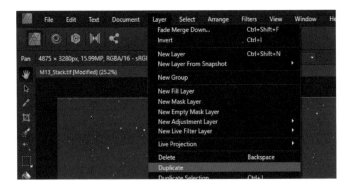

The image from the lower layer has now been copied to a new layer sandwiched between the two existing layers.

This new layer will be used to create a layer mask. This layer mask will prevent us seeing through to the brighter parts of the bottom image.

To prevent the mask from destroying fine detail in the image contained within the lower layer, we first need to blur this middle layer.

Click the middle layer to select it.

From the main menu, click **Filters > Blur > Gaussian Blur.**

Slide the adjustment until most of the stars are blurred out of existence as shown below. Some of the very bright stars may appear as very faint extended objects. This is expected.

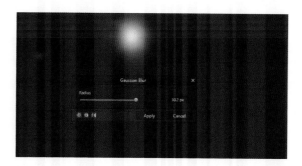

Click **Apply.**

The middle layer is now prepared and is ready to be converted into the layer mask.

Right-click on that middle layer and in the menu that appears, click **Rasterise to Mask.**

There should now be a small, shaded square in the bottom right of that layer, and (Mask) in the name indicating that it been converted to a layer mask.

To use this new layer mask, it needs to be applied to the layer above it. Put a tick in the box on the upper layer to make it visible.
(The fainter stars revealed in the lower layer will now disappear).

Grab the middle layer on the left-hand side using the mouse. Drag it up onto the layer above it, so that a vertical blue line appears on the side of the icon in the upper layer as shown below.

Release the layer and the mask will now be acting on the upper layer. There will only be two layers visible. The Layer Mask is now associated with the upper layer. It will be shown as another icon within the upper layer as shown below.

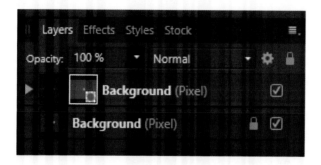

This new layer mask is now preventing you from seeing through to the brighter parts of the lower image and the over-exposed centre of the cluster, but still enable you to see the fainter stars and deep sky objects in that image.

The resulting image now show stars right into the bright core as well as the fainter stars at the extremities of the cluster easily visible extending away from it.

A Brief description of how a layer mask works.

A layer mask works by hiding any anything lying beneath that layer. In this case we used the information copied from the lower layer to act as our mask. Where that mask is white, the image is completely opaque. It effectively prevents you seeing anything through its associated layer. A completely black mask will make its associated image layer completely transparent, allowing you to see everything underneath. A pixel in the mask at the mid-grey point would be 50% opaque. The nearer a pixel in the mask is to the white end, the opaquer it becomes. The closer a pixel is to the black end, the more transparent it becomes. The level of grey that any pixel in the mask has, dictates how transparent that pixel becomes when applied in the mask. Our new mask enables us to see through the darker parts of the lower image but could not see the brighter parts. This layer mask enables us to carefully control what we want to reveal, or not, of the layer beneath it.

Once the image has been flattened you may need to use the Levels, Curves or Vibrance tool as before to add final touches to get a nicely balanced sky background and colour.

Multi-Layer Masking.

The layer masking technique shown above is great for many objects, but when imaging much brighter objects, like the Orion Nebula, or Andromeda Galaxy, the graduation between the differing brightness portions can be difficult to achieve using just one image and stretching it (although this can be achieved). For these objects, this technique works best if several images of differing exposures are taken. Some of short exposure will capture just the bright portions. Longer exposures will capture the fainter extensions. Ideally, a series of exposures in between these two would help to create a much smoother transition between the different areas of the object captured. When taking your images, use the usual method of stacking multiple Subs for each exposure.

Below are the 5 images of M42 that I will be using to demonstrate this method.

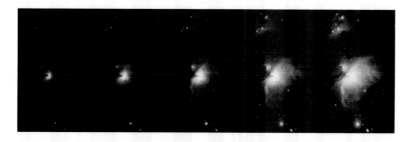

A Zip file of these images can be downloaded from my Web site:
www.star-gazing.co.uk/AffinityPhotoDownloads

I will let you into a secret here. Although it would have been best to take multi-exposure images for this, all these individual images were created from a single stacked image (The fainter one of the five). The other images were created using the curves, levels and plugins techniques shown earlier in this guide. I used different stretches, saving each result as a separate image. So, it is possible to produce an image showing the bright and faint portions of an object using just a single image stacked from several identical subs. These images will need to be imported into a stack.

From the menu, click **File > New Stack...**

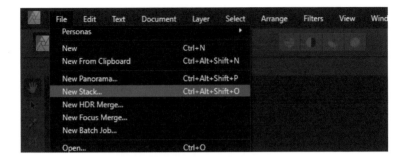

Make sure **Automatically Align Images** is unticked, as I have found this can cause some strange results.

Click the **Add** Button and go to the folder where the images for the stack are stored. In this case I am using the images of M42 shown above.

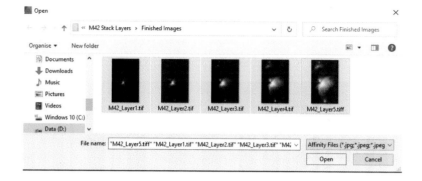

Select all the image files required to load into the stack.

Click **Open**.

The selected images will appear in the list.

Check that all the required files are included, then click **OK**.

The images will now be loaded into a **"Live Stack Group"** within Layers as shown below.

The images will need to be released from the stack group. To do this, click the left-hand mouse button on the triangle left of that layer. The images you imported into the stack are now visible as individual layers below the Live Stack Group.

Right-click the on the Live Stack Group and in the menu that appears, click **Ungroup.**

The images will have been removed from the Live Stack group and will be visible as separate layers within the stack.

These layers need to be arranged so that the brightest image is at the bottom of the stack, with the least bright image on the top. The other layers should follow in order of brightness.

Click to grab each layer in turn dragging the layers up and down the stack to achieve this as shown below.

Hold the mouse on the left-hand side of each layer as it is dragged.

Be careful as you do this. It is very easy to drag a layer "into" another one, to associate it with that layer. If the layer you are dragging does "disappear", look for a layer that has a triangle on it, which will indicate it has another layer "hidden" within it.
If this does happen, click on the triangle to reveal the hidden layer, and drag it back out.

Once all the layers are arranged in the correct order, everything is ready to create and start applying the layer masks for each layer.

A different layer mask needs to be created for each layer. The layer mask for each layer is created from the layer directly underneath it.
Some images will need to be aligned.
Press **Alt** and click on all the layers to select them.

From the main menu, select: **Arrange > Align Layers by Stars**. This will align all the layers. It is not really required for these images, as they are already aligned.

What follows next sounds quite complicated at first, but we are just following the same layer masking method shown previously using the M13 image. The only difference is that as the brightness of M42 is vastly different across the nebula. To achieve a good effect, we will need to work on multiple layers of differing brightness and work our way up the stack, masking each layer as we go.

Remove the tick on all the upper layers to hide them.
Leave a tick on the lower layer so that this is the only layer that is visible.

Click the right-hand mouse button on the bottom layer.

On the menu that appears, select **Duplicate.**
A copy of Layer 5 will be created between the first two layers.

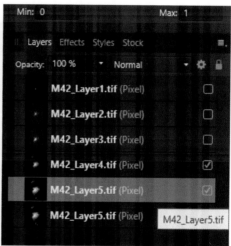

This newly created layer is going to be converted into our layer mask.

Firstly, a Gaussian Blur needs to be applied to the mask layer. This prevents it from hiding detail and stars we want to see in the lower image.

Click on the new layer mask layer to ensure it is selected.

From the menu, click **Filters > Blur > Gaussian Blur.**
You may need to experiment with all these settings to get the best possible result.

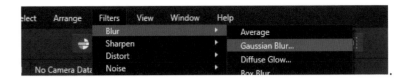

Drag the slider to the right-hand side to blur the layer mask until all the stars have been blurred out of existence. The nebula will become very blurry. The image should look something like that shown below.

Once happy with the amount the mask layer has been blurred, click **Apply.**

To create the layer mask, right-click the blurred mask layer.

From the menu that appears, click **Rasterise to Mask.**

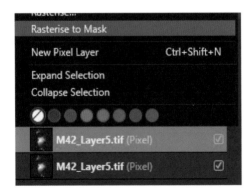

This layer should now be visible with a small, shaded square within its own icon, indicating that it has been converted into a layer mask.

The layer mask is now ready for use. It is not currently having much of an effect. It needs to be applied to the layer above it to have the masking effect required.

Put a tick back into the layer directly above the new layer mask to bring it back into view. Drag the layer mask onto the layer above it so that a vertical blue line appears next to the layer icon as shown below.

Release the layer and the layer mask should now be associated with image Layer 4. This layer should have a triangle and a small, shaded icon beside it, indicating that the new layer mask is now acting upon this image layer.

The effect of the layer mask should now be visible on the image. More of the brighter nebula in the central core is now visible, without being over-exposed. Much of the very bright over-exposed nebula contained in the lower image cannot be seen through the upper layer as the layer mask is preventing us from seeing through to it. You should also see that the fainter parts of the nebula are still visible as the mask is allowing you to view the fainter parts of the lower image.

At this stage we have successfully masked the lower layer, but we have 3 more layers above this layer mask. Each of these layers will need its own layer mask added to them to bring the rest of the bright parts of the nebula into view. It is important to remember that the mask for each subsequent layer is always created from the image layer lying directly beneath it.

To start the next layer mask, right-click the layer you have just added the mask to and click **Duplicate**. An identical layer will be created.

The new layer identical to Layer 4 is now visible complete with its own layer mask. For this layer to act as a new mask for the next layer above it, we need to delete this layer mask from it, as it is not required.

Click on the right-hand layer mask icon on the right in the new copied layer to highlight it as shown above. Press **Delete** to remove the mask from that new layer.

This layer should now be visible as a simple layer without an associated layer mask, as shown below.

We now follow the same routine as above on this new layer.

Untick the layer above this new layer to hide it. Blur the new layer using the same Gaussian Blur as before from menu, **Filters**.

You should now be able to select **Repeat Gaussian Blur** with a single click.

Once the layer has been blurred, right-click this new layer.
From the menu, select **Rasterise to Mask.** Drag this layer into the layer above, making sure a vertical blue line is visible before it is released.

Replace the tick on the next layer up to reveal it again.
Repeat this process for each layer as you make your way up the layer stack.
Just to recap the steps:

- Duplicate the masked layer below the next layer.
- Delete the layer mask from the new copied layer.
- Use a Gaussian blur on this layer.
- Rasterise to Mask.
- Drag the mask into the layer above.
- Repeat these steps on each of the layers moving upwards.

Once all layer masks have been applied to each layer, the final stack should appear something like the image below. All parts of the nebula should be visible with far less over-exposed areas in the bright centre with The Trapezium still visible within the bright core.

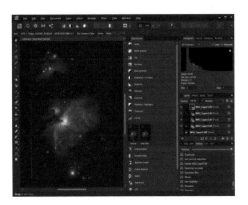

In some images, you may need to adjust the brightness of some of the layer masks to get a smoother transition between each layer.

To flatten the image and save or to export the image as a different image file type other than Affinity Photo, see the section on Managing Layers and Saving and Exporting Images.

Live Filter Layer Sharpening.

Some very subtle image sharpening can be achieved using a Live Filter layer. This is very useful for enhancing detail in nebulae, galaxies, and comet tails.

In this case I am using the processed image **Horsehead-Stack.tiff.**

Open the stacked and processed image in Photo Persona.

From the Menu, select **Layer > New Live Filter Layer > Sharpen:**

There are two Live Filter Layers we can use to achieve slightly different results; **Clarity** or **Unsharp Mask.**

Clarity.
Once clicked, a Clarity Live Filter layer is applied to the image.
Adjust the strength of the Clarity adjustment to sharpen the image.

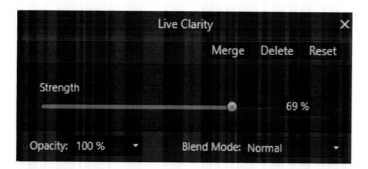

Unsharp Mask.
Again, once clicked a live filter layer using an unsharp mask filter is applied to the image.

Adjust the Radius and Factor sliders to achieve the desired effect.

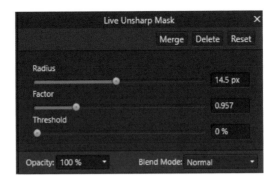

Once happy with either sharpening, click the cross top-right of the tool to close the Live Filter Layer window.

With both these techniques, like most things, they do come with a cost. They can create more noise. Be extremely careful not to over-sharpen the image. This will create unwanted and unsightly artifacts.

There is an extra amount of finer control of the sharpening created by the filter layer. This can be achieved by adjusting the Opacity of the Live Filter Layer to the image.

This further adjustment is accessed by single clicking on the Live Filter Layer to select it. The adjustment tool itself should not be open.

Below the layers tab, select the **Opacity** tool. Sliding it to the left will decrease the opacity of the Live Adjustment Layer, reducing the amount of sharpening applied to the image.

This gives very fine control over the amount of sharpening the adjustment layer applies to the underlying image.

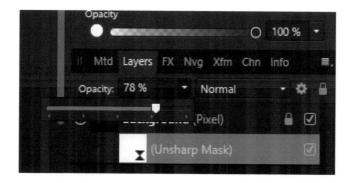

If you are adventurous, you may want to try a combination of the various sharpening methods to see if they get the most detail out of your images.

The image below shows the result of Live Filter Layer sharpening on the horsehead image using combination of Clarity and Unsharp Mask adjustments. Original image on the left, sharpened on the right.

Unsharp Masking.

This technique can also help to reveal more detail hidden within images. It stems from the old chemical processing days, where an out of focus mask was used when developing the film. Fortunately, digital technology makes this technique extremely easy in Affinity Photo.

Affinity Photo's method of unsharp masking is much simpler than the more involved method used in Photoshop.

The files used can be downloaded from my Web Site:
www.star-gazing.co.uk/AffinityPhotoDownloads

From the menu select, **Layer > New Live Filter Layer > Sharpen > Unsharp Mask...**

This opens the Unsharp Mask tool and inserts a Live Filter Layer into the existing layer.

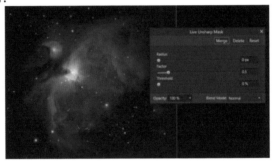

In the Live Unsharp Mask control, leave **Threshold** at 0%.
Move the **Radius** and **Factor** sliders to the right to sharpen the image and get the effect you like, ensuring you do not overdo it. Doing so will create artefacts in the image, adding detail that does not actually exist.

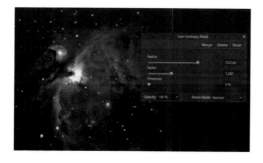

I would suggest moving the sliders just enough so that the image is just starting to look slightly over-sharpened.
Do not press any buttons to finish this adjustment yet, as we have still not finished using this tool.

Another adjustment will need to be applied to help soften the effect of the unsharp mask to bring back a more natural look to the image.
Click on the drop-down menu **Opacity.**

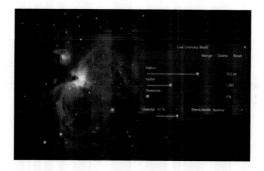

Slide the **Opacity** setting to the left to soften the effect of the Unsharp Mask on the image. This gives a little bit more fine control over the degree of sharpening.

When happy with the overall effect of the Unsharp Mask, click **Merge**.

Creating RGB and LRGB Images
RGB Images.

Affinity Photo makes it a little bit harder to create RGB images from monochrome tri-filter images than Photoshop. With Photoshop, you just copy and paste the images into their own colour channels. Here is the recommended was of creating LRGB images in Affinity Photo.

These images of M35 were taken with a monochrome CMOS camera using Red, Green and Blue filters. Several subs were taken with each colour filter. Each set of subs were stacked separately to produce a mono image, resulting in three images. One for Red, one for Blue and one for Green.

Open the three images in Affinity Photo.
Select one of the images as the working image.
I am going to choose the Red image, so ignore this image for now.

Select the Blue image and copy it by selecting **Edit > Copy** from the main menu.

Select the red image and click **Edit > Paste** from the menu.
This will add the Blue image as a separate layer on top of the red image.

Select the green image, copy it as before and paste that into the Red image as well. There should now be three layers visible under Layers. Each layer will be named **Background (Pixel)**.

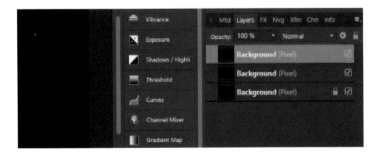

To save getting lost at this stage, double-click on each layer to name each layer to the colour each layer represents.

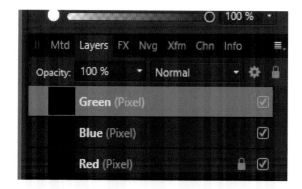

Each layer is currently 100% opaque, so neither the Blue nor Red image is seen as it is hidden behind the Green image.

We are going to change the properties of the two upper layers so that each layer contributes to the final image.

Hold down **Ctrl** and select the two upper layers, in this case Green & Blue.

Above the layers, open the drop-down menu which says **Normal**.

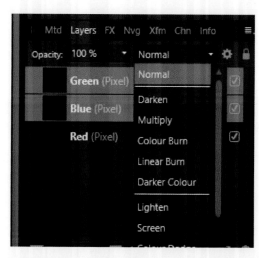

Select **Lighten** to convert both upper layers to Lighten layers. Once this is done, all three layers are contributing to the brightness of the resulting image.

The three images in the layer may not be precisely aligned. Affinity Photo includes a fantastic tool that enables this to be done with just a couple of clicks to align the images using the stars in the image.

Hold down **Ctrl** and click on each layer to select all three layers.

From the main menu and select go to **Arrange > Align Layers By Stars.**

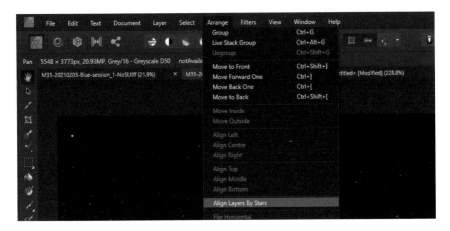

All three layers should now be perfectly aligned.

Everything is now ready to create the colour image.

As the original image was monochrome, for us to generate colour, the image will need to be converted to a colour image.

From the main menu select
Document > Convert Format / ICC Profile…

Change the file to the same bit format RGB image. In this case, this is a **Grey/16bit** image, so I will select the corresponding **RGB/16bit** image format to convert it to a colour image.

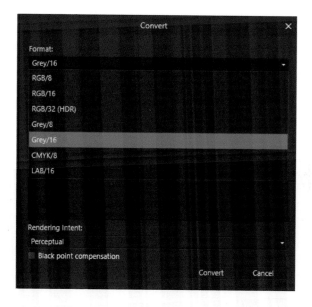

Click **Convert**.

Now we can create the colour using the information within the three monochrome images.

Click on the Red layer to select it.
Open the **Recolour** Tool and click on **Default** and the tool will appear.
It creates a red colour at 0° by default. The image will now appear red.

Click the cross top-right of the tool window to close the tool. The resulting Recolour adjustment layer can be seen sitting above the red layer within the layers stack.

This adjustment layer should only apply the colour change to the Red layer, so it will need to be moved so it is associated with that layer.

Using the mouse, grab hold of the Re-colour adjustment layer and drag it to where the name of the Red layer is as shown beside its icon. A blue horizontal line will appear when the Recolour Adjustment layer is in the correct position as shown below.

Release it and the Recolour Adjustment layer should now be associated and seen as a sub-layer with the Red layer.
There will be a triangle visible beside the Red image layer.

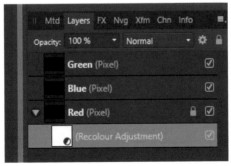

We now need to add a similar Recolour Adjustment layer to the Blue and Green layers to create their colour.

The simplest way to do this is to copy the Recolour Adjustment layer already created twice. Then drag those copies into the other two layers.

To do this, right-click on the Red Recolour Adjustment layer and click **Copy**.

Right-click again and select **Paste**. Repeat this step and there should now be three Recolour Adjustment Layers visible nested under the Red layer.

It does not matter which one is selected. Using the mouse, drag one of these new Recolour Adjustment Layers into the Blue and Green layers as before.

Once all the adjustment layers are in the correct positions, they should appear like this if the triangle is ticked and pointing down on each layer.

The image will appear extremely red at this stage. The Recolour adjustment layers currently created are each applying a red recolour to all three layers.

The Red layer is already showing the correct colour, so this does not need to be changed. The Blue and Green layers will need to be adjusted to show their true colour and add this to the final image.

Firstly, we will create the Green colour.
Double-click on the white square icon in the Recolour Adjustment Layer associated with the **Green Layer**. The Recolour Tool will open.

Move the Hue Slider to **120°** or type this value into the box on the right. Some green coloration will now be visible in the image.

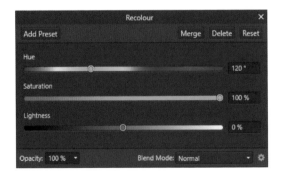

Click the cross top right of the tool to close the window.

Now to create the Blue colour.
Double-click on the white square icon in the Recolour Adjustment Layer associated with the Blue Layer. The Recolour Tool will open.
Move the Hue Slider to 240° or type this value into the box.

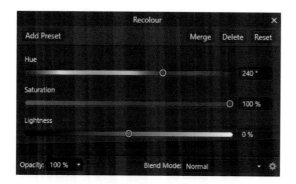

Click the cross to close the tool.

All three colours should have been applied correctly the image should now be a true colour image.

The resulting image can then be post-processed using curves and levels adjustment as required as shown in this guide.

Adding a Luminosity Layer to create an LRGB image.
If a Light image needs to be added to the RGB image to produce an LRGB image the process there is an extra process to follow.

Open the monochrome stacked image produced from subs taken that were taken using a clear filter (or no filter at all).

Copy the image and paste it on top of the RGB stack created previously. The image will go monochrome.

Hold down **Shift** and make sure all four layers are selected.

From the main menu, select **Arrange > Align Layers By Stars**
All three layers should now be accurately aligned with one another.

Click on the new upper layer to make sure that it is selected.

Click the drop-down menu Currently showing **Normal**.

Select **Luminosity** from the menu. This is now a LRGB Image.

This turns the top layer into a luminosity layer, which only contributes the brightness of the pixels to the resulting image. Only the layers below contribute towards colour data.

When an image has a luminosity layer above an image or stack beneath that is supplying the colour data changes need to be made on specific layers. If brightness changes need to be made to the image, this needs to be done to the upper Luminosity layer. Any colour or saturation adjustments will need to be applied to the lower layer.

If there are any artefacts around the edges caused by misalignment of the subs, this can be cropped out using the crop tool.

Creating Hubble Palette Images

The process, technique and settings used to create a Hubble Palette image is the same process as shown above for creating RGB images. The only difference is the filters used to take the original subs. Instead of using a Red, Green or Blue filter to create the three monochrome stacked images, the three filters used are SII, HA & OIII for the three colour channels.

The three resulting mono images are then placed into the stack with the following Recolour Adjustment Layers applied to the following images.

Red – SII (Sulphur). - Recolour Tool setting 0°.
Green – Ha (Hydrogen Alpha). - Recolour Tool setting 120°.
Blue – OIII (Oxygen III). - Recolour Tool setting 240°.

Once the images are stacked and colour rendered into their respective Red, Green and Blue layers following the RGB workflow above, an image with the Hubble Pallette will be produced.

This can then be processed further, using the techniques in this guide.

Combining Colour and Monochrome Images

The Star Alignment tool included with Affinity Photo makes it extremely easy to match up different image files. You might, for example, want to add some colour data to a monochrome image. I have done this frequently, taking a Hydrogen Alpha image with a monochrome camera and adding colour data from an old DSLR image. This technique works extremely well.

I have used the two images in the **Monkey-Head-Neb.zip** file to demonstrate this technique.

Open both images. Go to the coloured image and copy it. Paste it into the monochrome image. There will now be two layers visible in this image. The lower monochrome image and the upper colour image.

These two images are of different sizes. In this case, the colour image is much larger than the monochrome image. If the images are too different the star alignment tool will struggle. Only a small part of the colour image of The Monkey Head Nebula can be seen once it is pasted in. Click the **Move** tool button. Grab the corner of the colour image and drag it inwards to decrease the size of the colour image so that it just about fits within the lower image.

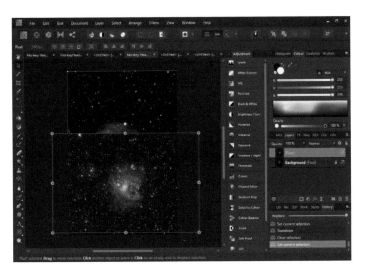

Now the two images are of a similar size, we will let the star alignment tool do its work. Make sure that both layers are selected by holding down shift and clicking on both layers.

From the main menu, select **Arrange > Align Layers by Stars**

If this option is greyed out, check that both layers have been selected.

Once **Align Layers by Stars** has been clicked, the two images should now have been resized and rotated and are superimposed.

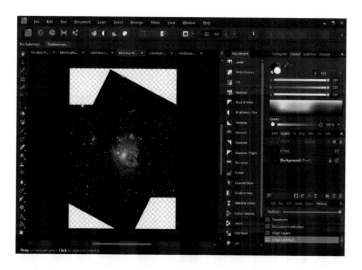

Use the crop tool to remove the blank outer edges.
In some cases, you may need to rotate the final image to get the best fit.

Now we need to swap the images around to get the best result.

In the Layers panel, drag the upper colour layer (called (Pixel)) so that it is laying underneath the lower Monochrome layer.

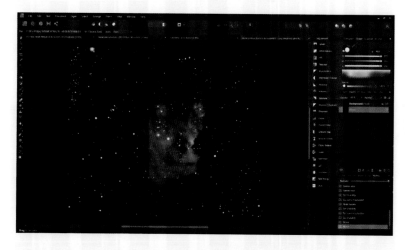

Click on the upper layer and in the layer panel from the drop-down menu which currently says **Normal**, change this layer type to **Luminosity**.

Once this is done, you should have all the quality of the monochrome image, with the colour data added from the image below.

Once again, any overlap issues, such as in the two corners of this image, can be cropped out.

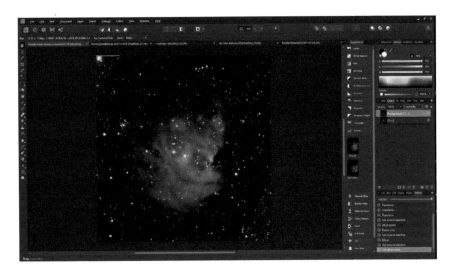

You may see some colour noise showing through from the lower image. Use the Gaussian Blur and Saturation techniques shown in this guide, to get rid of this colour noise and increase the colour visible in the image.

Opening Single Raw and FITS Files
Importing RAW Files.

If you have taken a single raw image using a DSLR these can be opened directly into Affinity Photo for processing. If the program is kept up to date it should be able to handle the latest raw file formats for newer cameras.

If Affinity Photo is set as the default program to open the raw files, the image will open directly into the **Develop Persona** as shown below.

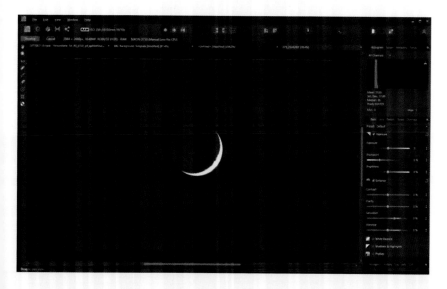

You do not have to make any changes at this point, as all adjustments can all be done from within the Photo Persona once the image has been imported.

There are several tools visible on the right-hand side of the screen.

These sliders can be used to adjust various aspects of the image, such as exposure, clarity, brightness, contrast, and saturation to show the image off at its best.

White Balance by default is unticked.
Tick this box to reveal two new sliders.
Use these to adjust the Temperature and Tint to get the best colour balance for the image.

One annoying feature of the Develop Persona is if you want to close a file before development is finished, say, if you opened the wrong image.
If the cross top-right to close the image is clicked, you get this message.

If you click the **Cancel** button instead, it gives this message.

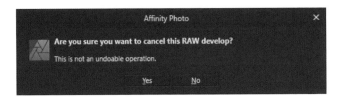

Serif should give you the option to stop these annoying nags.

Importing FITS Files.

FITS files are the raw files produced by CCD and CMOS Cameras. One-shot colour cameras will need to be debayered to obtain the colour from the tile.

Although Affinity Photo cannot open FITS files directly, the Astrophotography Stacking Persona gives us the ability to open them singly and then work on them directly within the Photo Persona.

To open a FITS file, from the main menu, click,

File > New Astrophotography Stack.

Under the files tab on the right-hand side of the window, (you may need to click on the tab to open it), click the **Add Files** button.

Browse to where the FITS file is located and double-click on the image.

The FITS file will open within the Astrophotography stacking Persona.

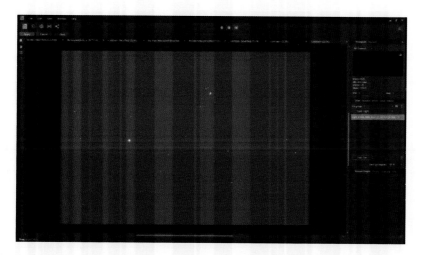

If the file is a colour image, under the **Raw Options** Tab, select the drop-down menu under **FITS Bayer pattern.**

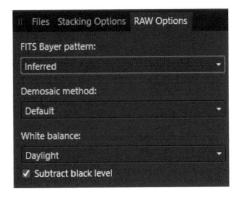

The default setting is **Inferred.**

From the drop-down menu, select the Bayer matrix pattern that gives the best colour for that image.

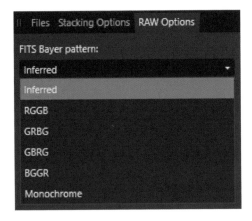

The colour will be previewed in the image once the Bayer pattern is selected.

Click the **Stack** button, wait a moment, then click **Apply**.

The FITS file will now open within Photo Persona for editing.

Flattening an Image

Sometimes a stack may need to be flattened to a single layer, so that another adjustment can be made on the completed image.

There are two ways of flattening an image.

Merge Selected.

This removes all the underlying layers to produce a single flat image from the result.

Select all the layers in the image by clicking on the top layer, press and hold down **Shift**, then click the bottom layer.

From the menu, select **Layer > Merge Selected.**

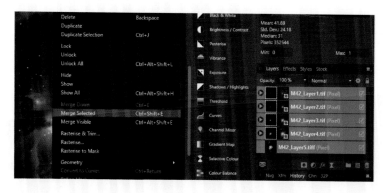

The flattened image will now show as single layer. The individual images that were used to create that image have been removed.

Only the single composite image remains as a single layer as shown below.

Merge Visible.

This second method of flattening leaves all the current layers in place and produces a flat image layer resulting from the layers, sitting above the layers. This is useful if you want to keep all the layers intact.

This will use the information from the visible layers, so selecting the layers is not required.

From the menu, select **Layer > Merge Visible.**

The flattened image will appear above the original stack of layers.

Once flattened, either of these final images produced may benefit from some final polishing using the techniques of curves, levels and saturation tools shown previously in this guide. Do not be afraid to do further processing on these flattened images. You may even build up further adjustment layers on these as you progress through the post-processing.

Reducing Stars.

It may take a bit of experimenting to the get this technique right for your images. Open the image and select the image layer containing the stars that need reducing. It may take a while to learn the best settings to use for your images.

From the main menu, click **Select > Select Sampled Colour**

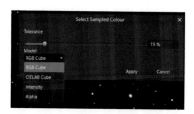

From the **Model** Drop-down menus, select **Intensity.**

Click on a bright star in the image and slide the **Tolerance** level up to select all the stars that need reducing. Click **Apply**.

From the main menu, click **Select > Grow/Shrink.**

Tick the **Circular** box and increase the size of the Radius to select a small area around each star that needs reducing. You may have to type a value in if the slider is too responsive. Click **Apply.**

From the main menu, click, **Layer > New Live Filter Layer > Blur > Minimum Blur.**

Tick **Circular.**

From the main menu, click**, Select > Deselect** to deselect the stars.

Slide the **Radius** slider to the right to reduce the stars. Again, if the slider is too responsive, type in the figure.

You can now process this image some more or flatten and save it.

Saving and Exporting Images.

If the layers in an image need to be preserved with the file, use **Save** or **Save As...** This will save the file as an Affinity Photo file and preserve all the layers by default.

Affinity Photo files have the file extension **.afphoto** and can only be opened using Affinity Photo.

If the image files need to be saved in a different image file format such as a TIF, PNG or JPG image for use on the Web, the image will need to be exported.

Important: Exporting images in certain file formats does not preserve the layers, or if they are opened in different image processing software. This is something to be aware of if you want to keep the layers intact within your image and share them.

Exporting is achieved from the menu, **File > Export**...
Select the image type to export the image from the menu that appears.

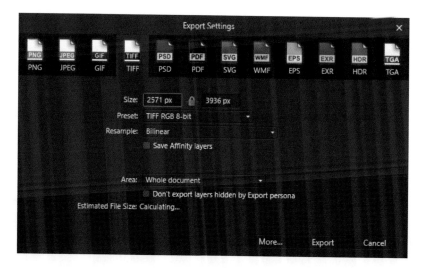

If required, the size and quality of the saved image can be made from this menu.

Changing the size is especially useful if the image needs to be changed to a smaller size for posting on The Web or on social media.

Click **Export** and choose the name of the image file before saving the image.

Another annoying feature of Affinity Photo is that it always defaults to the last folder that the previous image was saved in. So, you will need to watch where the new image is saved.

It would be better if the files were always saved in the same folder that the original image was loaded from.

Unless you know exactly which folder this is, it could fox you for a bit until you realise where your newly saved file has gone.

I hope that this guide has enabled you to become more familiar with the many tools used in Affinity Photo and has helped you get the best out of your astrophotography.

If I have made any mistakes in laying out this guide, or something is not quite as clearly laid out as I thought, please do let me know so I can improve future editions.

If you would like to practise on the images I used for the processing in this guide, they can be downloaded from my Web page:

www.star-gazing.co.uk/AffinityPhotoDownloads

Any amendments or corrections to this book will be posted on the same link above.

I am open to correspondence and love to hear from fellow astronomy enthusiasts, so if you have any questions, please do send me a message.

dave@star-gazing.co.uk

If you have found this guide useful, please do send me a testimonial, or post a good online review so I can add it to my Web site.

Thank you.

February 2021

Look out for my other astrophotography guides:
Guide to Photoshop Astrophotography Image Processing.
Guide to Deep Sky Stacker: Deep Sky Objects and Comet Images.
Guide to Imaging the Moon.
Guide to Solar Webcam Imaging.

These guides are available for purchase from my Web site:
http://www.star-gazing.co.uk/Shop

Workshops:
My hands-on astronomy and astrophotography workshops are available for booking from my Web site:
www.star-gazing.co.uk/Workshops.html

1-2-1 Tuition.
Details of my 1-2-1 astronomy and astrophotography tuition is here:
www.star-gazing.co.uk/121

Find or follow me online:
Web: www.star-gazing.co.uk
Facebook: https://www.facebook.com/Eagleseye45
Twitter: https://twitter.com/Dave_StarGeezer
Flickr: https://www.flickr.com/photos/eagleseyeonthesky
YouTube: http://www.youtube.com/DaveEagle-Star-Gazing

Guide to Affinity Photo Astrophotography Image Processing

2nd Edition.

Dave Eagle FRAS

www.star-gazing.co.uk

Printed in Great Britain
by Amazon